Table of Contents

Density

Which has the greater mass, air or lead? Most of you would answer lead, but actually this question does not have an answer. To compare these two things you need to now how much of each you have. A large amount of air could have a greater mass than a small amount of lead. To compare different things, we have to compare the masses of each that occupy the same space, or volume. This is called density.

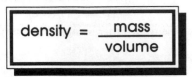

$$\text{density} = \frac{\text{mass}}{\text{volume}}$$

Solve the following problems.

1. What is the density of carbon dioxide gas if 0.196 g occupies a volume of 100 mL? _____

2. A block of wood 3.0 cm on each side has a mass of 27 g. What is the density of this block? _____

3. An irregularly shaped stone was lowered into a graduated cylinder holding a volume of water equal to 2.0 mL. The height of the water rose to 7.0 mL. If the mass of the stone was 25 g, what was its density? _____

4. A 10.0 cm³ sample of copper has a mass of 89.6 g. What is the density of copper? _____

5. Silver has a density of 10.5 g/cm³ and gold has a density of 19.3 g/cm³. Which would have a greater mass, 5 cm³ of silver or 5 cm³ of gold? _____

6. Five mL of ethanol has a mass of 3.9 g, and 5.0 mL of benzene has a mass of 4.4 g. Which liquid is denser? _____

7. A sample of iron has the dimensions of 2 cm x 3 cm x 2 cm. If the mass of this rectangular-shaped object is 94 g, what is the density of iron? _____

Determining Speed (Velocity)

Speed is a measure of how fast an object is moving or traveling. Velocity is a measure of how fast an object is traveling in a certain direction. Both speed and velocity include the distance traveled compared to the amount of time taken to cover this distance.

$$\text{speed} = \frac{\text{distance}}{\text{time}} \qquad \text{velocity} = \frac{\text{distance}}{\text{time}} \text{ in a specific direction}$$

Answer the following questions.

1. What is the velocity of a car that traveled a total of 75 kilometers north in 1.5 hours? _____

2. What is the velocity of a plane that traveled 3,000 miles from New York to California in 5.0 hours? _____

3. John took 45 minutes to bicycle to his grandmother's house, a total of four kilometers. What was his velocity in km/hr?

    _____

4. It took 3.5 hours for a train to travel the distance between two cities at a velocity of 120 miles/hr. How many miles lie between the two cities? _____

5. How long would it take for a car to travel a distance of 200 kilometers if it is traveling at a velocity of 55 km/hr?

    _____

6. A car is traveling at 100 km/hr. How many hours will it take to cover a distance of 750 km? _____

7. A plane traveled for about 2.5 hours at a velocity of 1200 km/hr. What distance did it travel? _____

8. A girl is pedaling her bicycle at a velocity of 0.10 km/min. How far will she travel in two hours? _____

Calculating Average Speed

Graph the following data on the grid below and answer the questions at the bottom of the page.

Time (min)	Distance (m)
0	0
1	50
2	75
3	90
4	110
5	125

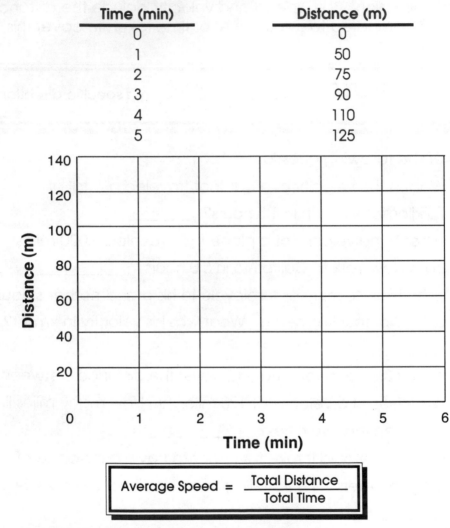

$$\text{Average Speed} = \frac{\text{Total Distance}}{\text{Total Time}}$$

1. What is the average speed after two minutes? _____
2. After three minutes? _____
3. After five minutes? _____
4. What is the average speed between two and four minutes? _____
5. What is the average speed between four and five minutes? _____

Acceleration Calculations

Acceleration means a change in speed or direction. It can also be defined as a change in velocity per unit of time.

$$a = \frac{v_f - v_i}{t} \quad \text{where} \quad \begin{aligned} a &= \text{velocity} \\ v_f &= \text{final velocity} \\ v_i &= \text{initial velocity} \\ t &= \text{time} \end{aligned}$$

Calculate the acceleration for the following data.

	Initial Velocity	Final Velocity	Time	Acceleration
1.	0 km/hr	24 km/hr	3 s	_____
2.	0 m/s	35 m/s	5 s	_____
3.	20 km/hr	60 km/hr	10 s	_____
4.	50 m/s	150 m/s	5 s	_____
5.	25 km/hr	1200 km/hr	2 min	_____

6. A car accelerates from a standstill to 60 km/hr in 10.0 seconds. What is its acceleration? _____

7. A car accelerates from 25 km/hr to 55 km/hr in 30 seconds. What is its acceleration? _____

8. A train is accelerating at a rate of 2.0 km/hr/s. If its initial velocity is 20 km/hr, what is its velocity after 30 seconds?

_____

9. A runner achieves a velocity of 11.1 m/s 9 s after he begins. What is his acceleration? _____ What distance did he cover? _____

Graphing Speed vs. Time

Plot the following data on the graph and answer the questions below.

Speed (km/hr)	Time (s)
0.0	0
10.0	2
20.0	4
30.0	6
40.0	8
50.0	10

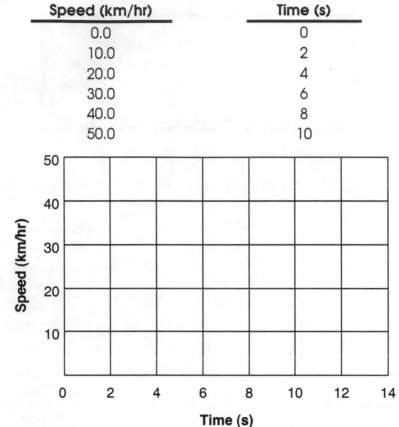

1. As time increases, what happens to the speed? _____

2. What is the speed at 5 s? _____

3. Assuming constant acceleration, what would be the speed at 14 s? _____

4. At what time would the object reach a speed of 45 km/hr? _____

5. What is the object's acceleration? _____

6. What would the shape of the graph be if a speed of 50.0 km/hr is maintained from 10 s to 20 s? _____

7. Based on the information in Problem 6, calculate the acceleration from 10 s to 20 s. _____

Graphing Distance vs. Time

Plot the following data on the graph and answer the questions below.

Distance (km)	Time (s)
0	0
5	10
12	20
20	30
30	40
42	50
56	60

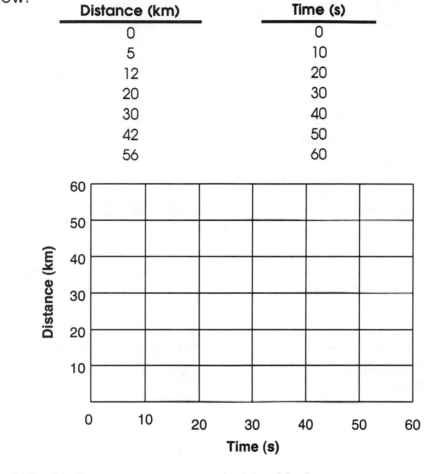

1.   What is the average speed at t = 20 s? _____

2.   What is the average speed at t= 30 s? _____

3.   What is the acceleration between 20 s and 30 s?

   _____

4.   What is the average speed at t = 40 s? _____

5.   What is the average speed at t = 60 s? _____

6.   What is the acceleration between 40 s and 60 s? _____

7.   Is the object accelerating at a constant rate? _____

Gravity and Acceleration (I)

The acceleration of a freely falling body is 9.8 m/sec/sec due to the force of gravity.

Using the formula, $a = \dfrac{v_f - v_i}{t}$, we can calculate the velocity of a falling object at any time if the initial velocity is known.

Example: What is the velocity of a rubber ball dropped from a building roof after 5 seconds?

Answer: $9.8 \text{ m/sec/sec} = \dfrac{v_f - 0}{5 \text{ sec}}$

$v_f = 49 \text{ m/sec}$

Solve the following problems.

1. What is the velocity of a quarter dropped from a tower after 10 seconds?

   _____

2. If a block of wood dropped from a tall building has attained a velocity of 78.4 m/s, how long has it been falling?

   _____

3. If a ball that is freely falling has attained a velocity of 19.6 m/s after two seconds, what is its velocity five seconds later?

   _____

4. A piece of metal has attained a velocity of 107.8 m/sec after falling for 10 seconds. What is its initial velocity?

   _____

5. How long will it take an object that falls from rest to attain a velocity of 147 m/sec?

   _____

Gravity and Acceleration (II)

The distance covered by a freely falling body is calculated by the following formula, $d = \dfrac{at^2}{2}$ where d = distance
a = acceleration
t = time

Example 1: How far will an object fall in 5 seconds?

Answer: $d = \dfrac{9.8 \text{ m/s}^2)\ (5s)^2}{2} = 122.5$ meters

Example 2: What is the average velocity of a ball that attains a velocity of 39.2 m/s after 4 seconds?

Answer: $v_a = \dfrac{v_f - v_i}{2} = \dfrac{39.2 - 0}{2} = 19.6$ m/s

---

Solve the following problems.

1. How far will a rubber ball fall in 10 seconds? _____

2. How far will a rubber ball fall in 20 seconds? _____

3. How long will it take an object dropped from a window to fall a distance of 78.4 meters? _____

4. Calculate the final velocity of the ball In Problem 1.

   _____

5. What is the average velocity of the ball in Problem 1?

   _____

6. An airplane is traveling at an altitude of 31,360 meters. A box of supplies is dropped from its cargo hold. How long will it take to reach the ground? _____

7. At what velocity will the box in Problem 6 be traveling when it hits the ground? _____

8. What is the average velocity of the box in Problem 6?

   _____

Force Diagrams

Find the resultant force in each of the following diagrams and draw the resultant vector. Use a ruler and a protractor where necessary. Scale: 1 cm = 10 N, where N represents newtons of force.

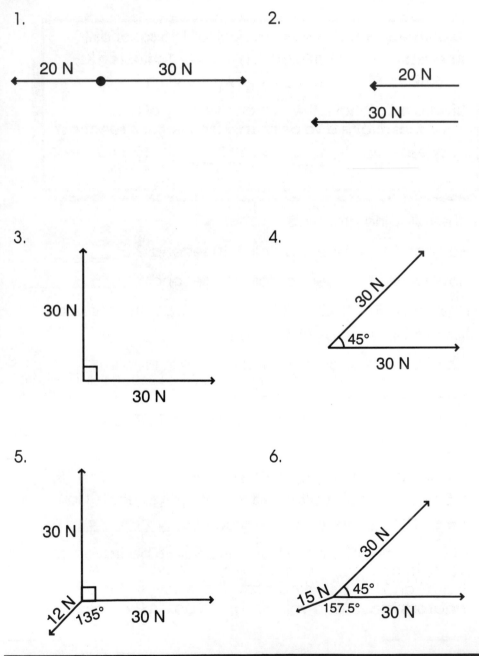

1.

20 N   30 N

2.

20 N

30 N

3.

30 N

30 N

4.

30 N

45°

30 N

5.

30 N

12 N 135°   30 N

6.

30 N

15 N 45°

157.5°   30 N

Force and Acceleration

A force is a push or a pull. To calculate force, we use the following formula, $F = ma$ where   F = force in newtons

m = mass in kg

a = acceleration in m/sec²

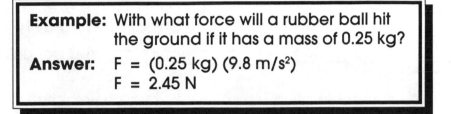

Example: With what force will a rubber ball hit the ground if it has a mass of 0.25 kg?

Answer: $F = (0.25 \text{ kg}) (9.8 \text{ m/s}^2)$
$F = 2.45 \text{ N}$

Solve the following problems.

1. With what force will a car hit a tree if the car has a mass of 3,000 kg and it is accelerating at a rate of 2 m/s²?

_____

2. A 10 kg bowling ball would require what force to accelerate it down an alleyway at a rate of 3 m/s²?

_____

3. What is the mass of a falling rock if it hits the ground with a force of 147 newtons?

_____

4. What is the acceleration of a softball if it has a mass of 0.50 kg and hits the catcher's glove with a force of 25 newtons?

_____

5. What is the mass of a truck if it is accelerating at a rate of 5 m/s² and hits a parked car with a force of 14,000 newtons?

_____

Motion Matching

Match the correct term in Column I with its definition in Column II.

I	II
I	**II**

I

1. ___ kinetic

2. ___ centripetal

3. ___ mass

4. ___ acceleration

5. ___ velocity

6. ___ weight

7. ___ gravity

8. ___ inertia

9. ___ speed

10. ___ momentum

11. ___ newton

II

a) amount of matter in an object

b) amount of force exerted on an object due to gravity

c) distance covered per unit of time

d) rate at which velocity changes over time

e) speed in a given direction

f) unit of measurement for force

g) energy of motion

h) tendency of a moving object to keep moving

i) depends on the mass and velocity of an object

j) type of force that keeps objects moving in a circle

k) attractive force between two objects

Heat Calculations

Heat is measured in units of joules or calories. The amount of heat given off or absorbed can be calculated by the following formula.

$\Delta Q = m \times \Delta T \times C$
heat = (mass in grams) (temperature change) (specific heat)
The specific heat of water = 1.0 cal/g C° or 4.2 joules/g C°

Solve the following problems.

1. How many calories are absorbed by a pot of water with a mass of 500 g in order to raise the temperature from 20° C to 30° C?

_____

2. How many joules would be absorbed for the water in Problem 1?

_____

3. If the specific heat of iron = 0.46 J/g C°, how much heat is needed to warm 50 g of iron from 20° C to 100° C?

_____

4. If it takes 105 calories to warm 100 g of aluminum from 20° C to 25° C, what is the specific heat of aluminum?

_____

5. If it takes 31,500 joules of heat to warm 750 g of water, what was the temperature change?

_____

Heat and Phase Changes

During a phase change, the temperature remains the same. For these calculations, we use the following formulas.

> For freezing and melting,
>   heat = (mass in grams) (heat of fusion)
> For boiling and condensation,
>   heat = (mass in grams) (heat of vaporization)
> The heat of fusion of water = 340 J/g
> The heat of vaporization of water = 2,300 J/g

Solve the following problems.

1. How many joules of heat are necessary to melt 500 g of ice at its freezing point?

   _____

2. How many kilojoules is this?

   _____

3. How much heat is necessary to vaporize 500 g of water at its boiling point?

   _____

4. If 5,100 joules of heat are given off when a sample of water freezes, what is the mass of the water?

   _____

5. If 57,500 joules of heat are given off when a sample of steam condenses, what is the mass of the steam?

   _____

Simple Machines

What types of simple machines are shown in the following pictures?

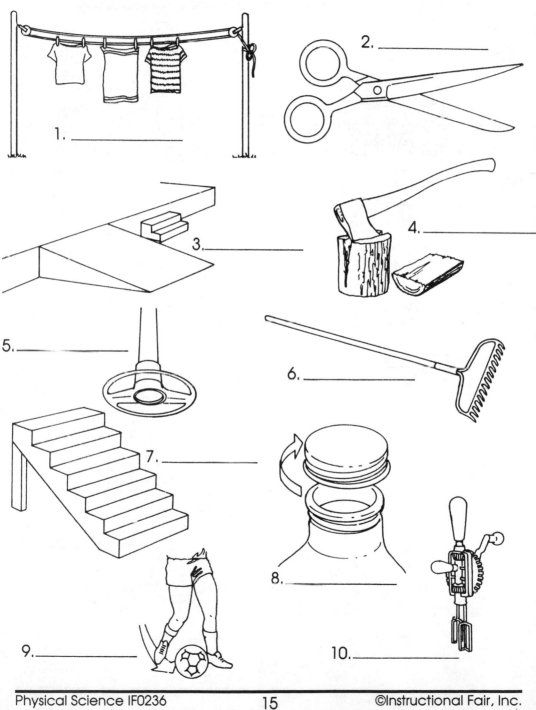

1. _____

2. _____

3. _____

4. _____

5. _____

6. _____

7. _____

8. _____

9. _____

10. _____

Types of Levers

Classify the following levers as first, second or third class.

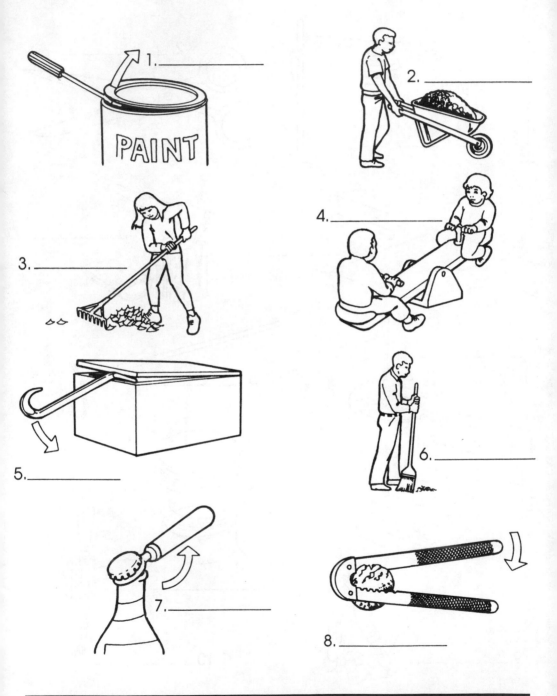

1. _____

2. _____

3. _____

4. _____

5. _____

6. _____

7. _____

8. _____

Potential and Kinetic Energy

Potential energy is stored energy due to position. Kinetic energy is energy that depends on mass and velocity (movement).

> Potential Energy = Weight x Height (P.E. = w x h)
> Kinetic Energy = $\frac{1}{2}$ Mass x Velocity^2 (K.E. = $\frac{1}{2}mv^2$)
> The units used are: Energy = joules
>   Weight = newtons
>   Height = meters
>   Mass = kilograms
>   Velocity = m/s

For a closed system, the sum of the potential energy and the kinetic energy is a constant. As the potential energy decreases, the kinetic energy increases.

Solve the following problems.

1. What is the potential energy of a rock that weighs 100 newtons that is sitting on top of a hill 300 meters high?

    _____

2. What is the kinetic energy of a bicycle with a mass of 14 kg traveling at a velocity of 3 m/s? _____

3. A flower pot weighing 3 newtons is sitting on a windowsill 30 meters from the ground. Is the energy of the flower pot potential or kinetic? _____ How many joules is this?

    _____

4. When the flower pot in Problem 3 is only 10 meters from the ground, what is its potential energy? _____

5. How much of the total energy in Problems 3 and 4 has been transformed to kinetic energy? _____

6. A 1200 kg automobile is traveling at a velocity of 100 m/s. Is its energy potential or kinetic? _____ How much energy does it possess? _____

Calculating Work

Work has a special meaning in science. It is the product of the force applied to an object and the distance the object moves. The unit of work is the joule (J).

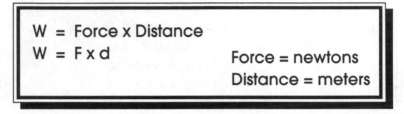

W = Force x Distance
W = F x d

Force = newtons
Distance = meters

Solve the following problems.

1. A book weighing 1.0 newton is lifted 2 meters. How much work was done?

   _____

2. A force of 15 newtons is used to push a box along the floor a distance of 3 meters. How much work was done?

   _____

3. It took 50 joules to push a chair 5 meters across the floor. With what force was the chair pushed?

   _____

4. A force of 100 newtons was necessary to lift a rock. A total of 150 joules of work was done. How far was the rock lifted?

   _____

5. It took 500 newtons of force to push a car 4 meters. How much work was done?

   _____

6. A young man exerted a force of 9,000 newtons on a stalled car but was unable to move it. How much work was done?

   _____

Mechanical Advantage

What is the mechanical advantage of the following simple machines?

$$MA = \frac{F_R}{F_E} \qquad \text{where } F_R = \text{resistance force}$$
$$F_E = \text{effort force}$$

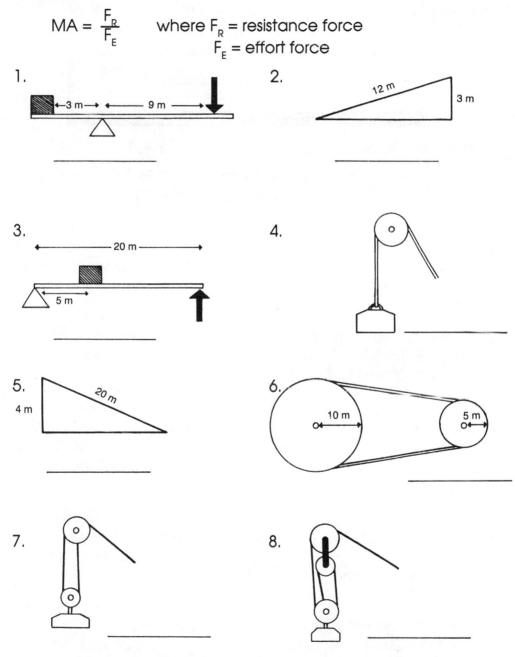

1.

────────

2.

12 m

3 m

────────

3.

20 m

5 m

────────

4.

────────

5.

20 m

4 m

────────

6.

10 m

5 m

────────

7.

────────

8.

────────

Calculating Efficiency

The amount of work obtained from a machine is always less than the amount of work put into it. This is because some of the work is lost due to friction. The efficiency of a machine can be calculated using the following formula.

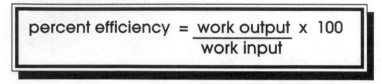

$$\text{percent efficiency} = \frac{\text{work output}}{\text{work input}} \times 100$$

What is the efficiency of the following machines?

1. A man expends 100 J of work to move a box up an inclined plane. The amount of work produced is 80 J.

   _____

2. A box weighing 100 newtons is pushed up an inclined plane that is 5 meters long. It takes a force of 75 newtons to push it to the top, which has a height of 3 meters.

   _____

3. Using a lever, a person applies 60 newtons of force and moves the lever 1 meter. This moves a 200 newton rock at the other end by 0.2 meters.

   _____

4. A person in a wheelchair exerts a force of 25 newtons to go up a ramp that is 10 meters long. The weight of the person and wheelchair is 60 newtons and the height of the ramp is 3 meters.

   _____

5. A boy pushes a lever down 2 meters with a force of 75 newtons. The box at the other end with a weight of 50 newtons moves up 2.5 meters.

   _____

6. A pulley system operates with 40% efficiency. If the work put in is 200 joules, how much useful work is produced?

   _____

Calculating Power

Power is the amount of work done per unit of time. The unit for power, joules/second, is the watt.

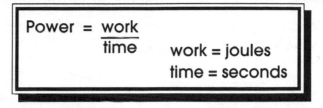

Power = work / time

work = joules
time = seconds

Solve the following problems.

1. A set of pulleys is used to lift a piano weighing 1,000 newtons. The piano is lifted 3 meters in 60 seconds. How much power is used?

    _____

2. How much power is used if a force of 35 newtons is used to push a box a distance of 10 meters in 5 seconds?

    _____

3. What is the power of a kitchen blender if it can perform 3,750 joules of work in 15 seconds?

    _____

4. How much work is done using a 500-watt microwave oven for 5 minutes?

    _____

5. How much work is done using a 60-watt light bulb for 1 hour?

    _____

Substances vs. Mixtures

A substance is matter for which a chemical formula can be written. Elements and compounds are substances. Mixtures can be in any proportion, and the parts are not chemically bonded.

Classify the following as to whether it is a substance or a mixture by writing S or M in the space provided.

1. sodium _____

2. water _____

3. soil _____

4. coffee _____

5. oxygen _____

6. alcohol _____

7. carbon dioxide _____

8. cake batter _____

9. air _____

10. soup _____

11. iron _____

12. salt water _____

13. ice cream _____

14. nitrogen _____

15. eggs _____

16. blood _____

17. table salt _____

18. nail polish _____

19. milk _____

20. cola _____

Homogeneous vs. Heterogeneous Matter

Classify the following substances and mixtures as either homogeneous or heterogeneous. Place a √ in the correct column.

	HOMOGENEOUS	HETEROGENEOUS
1. flat soda pop		
2. cherry vanilla ice cream		
3. salad dressing		
4. sugar		
5. soil		
6. aluminum foil		
7. black coffee		
8. sugar water		
9. city air		
10. paint		
11. alcohol		
12. iron		
13. beach sand		
14. pure air		
15. spaghetti sauce		

Physical vs. Chemical Properties

A physical property is observed with the senses and can be determined without destroying the object. For example, color, shape, mass, length, density, specific heat and odor are all examples of physical properties.

A chemical property indicates how a substance reacts with something else. When a chemical property is observed, the original substance is changed into a different substance. For example, the ability of iron to rust is a chemical property. The iron has reacted with oxygen and the original iron metal is gone. It is now iron oxide, a new substance. All chemical changes include physical changes.

Classify the following properties as either chemical or physical by putting a check in the appropriate column.

	Physical Property	Chemical Property
1. red color		
2. density		
3. flammability		
4. solubility		
5. reacts with acid to form hydrogen		
6. supports combustion		
7. bitter taste		
8. melting point		
9. reacts with water to form a gas		
10. reacts with a base to form water		
11. hardness		
12. boiling point		
13. can neutralize a base		

Physical vs. Chemical Change

In a physical change, the original substance still exists, it has only changed in form. Energy changes usually do not accompany physical changes, except in phase changes and when substances dissolve.

In a chemical change, a new substance is produced. Energy changes always accompany chemical changes. Chemical changes are always accompanied by physical changes.

Classify the following as examples of a physical change, a chemical change or both kinds of change.

1. Sodium hydroxide dissolves in water. _____

2. Hydrochloric acid reacts with
   sodium hydroxide to produce
   a salt, water and heat. _____

3. A pellet of sodium is sliced in two. _____

4. Water is heated and changed
   to steam. _____

5. Potassium chlorate decomposes
   to potassium chloride and
   oxygen gas. _____

6. Iron rusts. _____

7. Ice melts. _____

8. Acid on limestone produces
   carbon dioxide gas. _____

9. Milk sours. _____

10. Wood rots. _____

Elements and Their Symbols

Write the symbols for the following elements.

1. oxygen _____   11. magnesium _____

2. hydrogen _____   12. manganese _____

3. chlorine _____   13. neon _____

4. sodium _____   14. bromine _____

5. fluorine _____   15. phosphorus _____

6. carbon _____   16. silver _____

7. helium _____   17. lead _____

8. nitrogen _____   18. iron _____

9. copper _____   19. calcium _____

10. sulfur _____   20. potassium _____

Write the name of the element that corresponds to each of the following symbols.

21. Cu _____   31. Ca _____

22. K _____   32. Ag _____

23. C _____   33. P _____

24. Au _____   34. O _____

25. Zn _____   35. I _____

26. Pb _____   36. Sn _____

27. Fe _____   37. H _____

28. Na _____   38. F _____

29. S _____   39. Ni _____

30. Al _____   40. Hg _____

Parts of an Atom

An atom is made up of protons and neutrons which are in the nucleus, and electrons which are in the electron cloud surrounding the atom.

The atomic number equals the number of protons. The electrons in a neutral atom equal the number of protons. The mass number equals the sum of the protons and neutrons.

The charge indicates the number of electrons that have been lost or gained. A positive charge indicates the number of electrons (which are negatively charged) lost. A negative charge indicates the number of electrons gained.

This structure can be written as part of a chemical symbol.

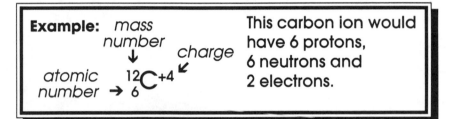

Example: *mass number* ↓ *charge* ↙ *atomic number* → $^{12}_{6}C^{+4}$

This carbon ion would have 6 protons, 6 neutrons and 2 electrons.

Complete the following chart.

Element/ Ion	Atomic Number	Mass Number	Charge	Protons	Neutrons	Electrons
1. $^{24}_{12}Mg$						
2. $^{39}_{19}K$						
3. $^{23}_{11}Na^{+1}$						
4. $^{19}_{9}F^{-1}$						
5. $^{27}_{13}Al^{+3}$						
6. $^{1}_{1}H$						
7. $^{24}Mg^{2+}$						
8. Ag						
9. S^{-2}						
10. $^{2}_{1}H$						
11. $^{35}Cl^{-}$						
12. Be^{2+}						

Bohr Models

Draw Bohr models of the following atoms.

1. $^{1}_{1}H$

2. $^{4}_{2}He$

3. $^{7}_{3}Li$

4. $^{23}_{11}Na$

5. $^{35}_{17}Cl$

6. $^{64}_{29}Cu$

28

Properties of Metals and Nonmetals

For the following physical and chemical properties, put a check in the appropriate column if it applies to a metal or a nonmetal.

Property	Metal	Nonmetal
1. malleable		
2. lustrous		
3. gaseous at room temperature		
4. forms negative ions		
5. metallic bonding		
6. more than 4 valence electrons		
7. conducts electricity in solid state		
8. ductile		
9. brittle		
10. only forms positive ions		
11. nonconductor		
12. covalent bonding		
13. can have both positive and negative oxidation numbers		
14. gives away electrons in chemical reactions		
15. prefers to receive electrons in chemical reactions		

Activity of the Elements

Since metals prefer to give away electrons during chemical bonding, the most active metals are closest to francium, which is a large atom with low ionization energy and electronegativity. Nonmetals prefer to pull in electrons, so the most active nonmetals are closest to fluorine, which has a high ionization energy and electronegativity. The noble gases (Group 18) are considered inactive since they already have a stable octet of electrons in their outer shell.

Referring to a periodic table, circle the member of each pair of elements which is most chemically active.

1.	Li and Na	16.	Cl_2 and Br_2
2.	Cl_2 and F_2	17.	Xe and I_2
3.	N_2 and Ne	18.	Fe and Ra
4.	Rb and Ca	19.	Sr and Mn
5.	Ti and Ca	20.	K and Na
6.	K and Mg	21.	Au and Mg
7.	O_2 and S	22.	S and Rn
8.	I_2 and Br_2	23.	Li and Be
9.	Na and Zn	24.	Se and Br_2
10.	P and S	25.	I_2 and F_2
11.	N_2 and O_2	26.	Rb and Sr
12.	Cl_2 and Ar	27.	Ba and Ra
13.	Ba and Fr	28.	Na and Mg
14.	Rb and Cu	29.	Te and I_2
15.	Be and Cr	30.	Ca and Rn

Periodic Table Puzzle

Group Number

1	2	3	4	5	6	7	8	9	10	11	12	13	14	15	16	17	18
I																	
	F														G	H	
													B				A
C							E					J					

		D												

Place the letter of each of the above elements next to its description below. Each answer may be used only once, so choose the best answer in each case.

1. An alkali metal _____

2. An alkaline earth metal _____

3. An inactive gas _____

4. An active nonmetal _____

5. A semimetal _____

6. An inner transition element _____

7. Its most common oxidation state is -2. _____

8. A metal with more than one oxidation state _____

9. Metal with an oxidation number of +3 _____

10. Has oxidation numbers of +1 and -1 _____

Types of Chemical Bonds

Classify the following compounds as ionic (metal and nonmetal), covalent (nonmetal and nonmetal) or both (compound containing a polyatomic ion).

1. $CaCl_2$ _____

2. CO_2 _____

3. H_2O _____

4. $BaSO_4$ _____

5. K_2O _____

6. NaF _____

7. Na_2CO_3 _____

8. CH_4 _____

9. SO_3 _____

10. LiBr _____

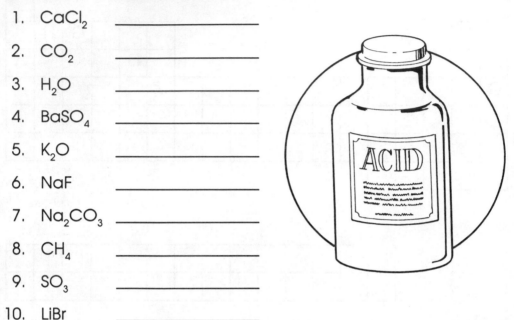

ACID

11. MgO _____

12. NH_4Cl _____

13. HCl _____

14. KI _____

15. NaOH _____

16. NO_2 _____

17. $AlPO_4$ _____

18. $FeCl_3$ _____

19. P_2O_5 _____

20. N_2O_3 _____

Number of Atoms in a Formula

Determine the number of atoms in the following chemical formulas.

1. $NaCl$ _____

2. H_2SO_4 _____

3. KNO_3 _____

4. $CaCl_2$ _____

5. C_2H_6 _____

6. $Ba(OH)_2$ _____

7. NH_4Br _____

8. $Ca_3(PO_4)_2$ _____

9. $Al_2(SO_4)_3$ _____

10. $Mg(NO_3)_2$ _____

11. $Cu(NO_3)_2$ _____

12. $KMnO_4$ _____

13. H_2O_2 _____

14. H_3PO_4 _____

15. $(NH_4)_3PO_4$ _____

16. Fe_2O_3 _____

17. $NaC_2H_3O_2$ _____

18. $Mg(C_2H_3O_2)_2$ _____

19. Hg_2Cl_2 _____

20. K_2SO_3 _____

Gram Formula Mass

Determine the gram formula mass of each of the following compounds.

1. $NaCl$ _____

2. H_2SO_4 _____

3. KNO_3 _____

4. $CaCl_2$ _____

5. C_2H_6 _____

6. $Ba(OH)_2$ _____

7. NH_4Br _____

8. $Ca_3(PO_4)_2$ _____

9. $Al_2(SO_4)_3$ _____

10. $Mg(NO_3)_2$ _____

11. $Cu(NO_3)_2$ _____

12. $KMnO_4$ _____

13. H_2O_2 _____

14. H_3PO_4 _____

15. $(NH_4)_3PO_4$ _____

16. Fe_2O_3 _____

17. $NaC_2H_3O_2$ _____

18. $Mg(C_2H_3O_2)_2$ _____

19. Hg_2Cl_2 _____

20. K_2SO_3 _____

Percentage Composition

Solve the following problems.

1. What is the percentage of carbon in CO_2?

   _____

2. How many grams of carbon are in 25 g of CO_2?

   _____

3. What is the percentage of sodium in NaCl?

   _____

4. How many grams of sodium are in 75 g of NaCl?

   _____

5. What is the percentage of oxygen in $KClO_3$?

   _____

6. How many grams of oxygen can be obtained from 5.00 g of $KClO_3$?

   _____

7. What is the percentage of silver in $AgNO_3$?

   _____

8. How many grams of silver can be recovered from 125 g of $AgNO_3$?

   _____

9. What is the percentage of gold in $AuCl_3$?

   _____

10. How many grams of gold can be recovered from 35.0 g of $AuCl_3$?

   _____

Writing Binary Formulas

Write the formulas for the compounds formed from the following ions.

1. Na^+, Cl^- _____

2. Ba^{+2}, F^- _____

3. K^+, S^{-2} _____

4. Li^+, Br^- _____

5. Al^{+3}, I^- _____

6. Zn^{+2}, S^{-2} _____

7. Ag^+, O^{-2} _____

8. Mg^{+2}, P^{-3} _____

9. Ni^{+2}, O^{-2} _____

10. Ni^{+3}, O^{-2} _____

11. Fe^{+2}, O^{-2} _____

12. Fe^{+3}, O^{-2} _____

13. Cr^{+2}, S^{-2} _____

14. Cr^{+3}, S^{-2} _____

15. Cu^+, Cl^- _____

16. Cu^{+2}, Cl^- _____

17. Pb^{+2}, O^{-2} _____

18. Pb^{+4}, O^{-2} _____

19. Mn^{+2}, Br^- _____

20. Mn^{+4}, Br^- _____

Naming Binary Compounds (Ionic)

Name the following ionic compounds using Roman numerals where necessary.

1. $BaCl_2$ _____

2. NaF _____

3. Ag_2O _____

4. CuBr _____

5. $CuBr_2$ _____

6. FeO _____

7. Fe_2O_3 _____

8. MgS _____

9. Al_2O_3 _____

10. CaI_2 _____

11. K_2S _____

12. $CrCl_2$ _____

13. $CrCl_3$ _____

14. CaO _____

15. Ba_3P_2 _____

16. Hg_2I_2 _____

17. Na_2O _____

18. BeS _____

19. MnO _____

20. Mn_2O_3 _____

Naming Binary Compounds (Covalent)

Name the following compounds using the prefix method.

1. CO _____

2. CO_2 _____

3. SO_2 _____

4. NO_2 _____

5. N_2O _____

6. SO_3 _____

7. CCl_4 _____

8. NO _____

9. N_2O_5 _____

10. P_2O_5 _____

11. N_2O_4 _____

12. CS_2 _____

13. OF_2 _____

14. PCl_3 _____

15. PBr_5 _____

Formulas With Polyatomic Ions

Matching the horizontal and vertical axes, write the formulas of the compounds with the following combination of ions. The first one is done for you.

	OH^-	NO_3^-	CO_3^{-2}	SO_4^{-2}	PO_4^{-3}
1. H^+	HOH (H_2O)	HNO_3	H_2CO_3	H_2SO_4	H_3PO_4
2. Na^+					
3. Mg^{+2}					
4. NH_4^+					
5. Ca^{+2}					
6. K^+					
7. Al^{+3}					
8. Pb^{+4}					

Naming of Non-Binary Compounds

An ionic compound that contains more than two elements must contain a polyatomic ion. Name the following compounds.

1. $NaNO_3$ _____

2. $Ca(OH)_2$ _____

3. K_2CO_3 _____

4. NH_4Cl _____

5. $MgSO_4$ _____

6. $AlPO_4$ _____

7. $(NH_4)_2SO_4$ _____

8. Na_3PO_4 _____

9. $CuSO_4$ _____

10. NH_4OH _____

11. Li_2SO_3 _____

12. $Mg(NO_3)_2$ _____

13. $Al(OH)_3$ _____

14. $(NH_4)_3PO_4$ _____

15. KOH _____

16. $Ca(NO_3)_2$ _____

17. K_2SO_4 _____

18. $Pb(OH)_2$ _____

19. Na_2O_2 _____

20. $CuCO_3$ _____

Naming Compounds (Mixed)

Name the following compounds.

1. NaCl _____

2. MnS _____

3. K_2O _____

4. $CuBr_2$ _____

5. CuBr _____

6. CO_2 _____

7. $PbSO_4$ _____

8. Li_2CO_3 _____

9. Na_2CO_3 _____

10. NO_2 _____

11. N_2O_4 _____

12. $Ca(OH)_2$ _____

13. NH_4Cl _____

14. SO_3 _____

15. $AlPO_4$ _____

16. CCl_4 _____

17. CaS _____

18. NH_3 _____

19. MgI_2 _____

20. K_3PO_4 _____

Writing Formulas From Names

Write the formulas for the following compounds.

1. carbon monoxide _____

2. sodium chloride _____

3. carbon tetrachloride _____

4. magnesium bromide _____

5. aluminum iodide _____

6. hydrogen hydroxide _____

7. iron (II) fluoride _____

8. carbon dioxide _____

9. sodium carbonate _____

10. ammonium sulfide _____

11. iron (II) oxide _____

12. iron (III) oxide _____

13. magnesium sulfate _____

14. sodium phosphate _____

15. dinitrogen pentoxide _____

16. phosphorus trichloride _____

17. aluminum sulfite _____

18. copper (I) carbonate _____

19. potassium hydrogen carbonate _____

20. sulfur trioxide _____

Balancing Equations

Balance the following chemical equations.

1. $CH_4 + O_2 \rightarrow CO_2 + H_2O$

2. $Na + I_2 \rightarrow NaI$

3. $N_2 + O_2 \rightarrow N_2O$

4. $N_2 + H_2 \rightarrow NH_3$

5. $KI + Cl_2 \rightarrow KCl + I_2$

6. $HCl + Ca(OH)_2 \rightarrow CaCl_2 + H_2O$

7. $KClO_3 \rightarrow KCl + O_2$

8. $K_3PO_4 + HCl \rightarrow KCl + H_3PO_4$

9. $S + O_2 \rightarrow SO_3$

10. $KI + Pb(NO_3)_2 \rightarrow KNO_3 + PbI_2$

11. $CaSO_4 + AlBr_3 \rightarrow CaBr_2 + Al_2(SO_4)_3$

12. $H_2O_2 \rightarrow H_2O + O_2$

13. $Na + H_2O \rightarrow NaOH + H_2$

14. $C_2H_6 + O_2 \rightarrow CO_2 + H_2O$

15. $Mg(NO_3)_2 + K_3PO_4 \rightarrow Mg_3(PO_4)_2 + KNO_3$

WORD EQUATIONS

Write and balance the following chemical equations.

1. Hydrogen plus oxygen yield water.

2. Nitrogen plus hydrogen yield ammonia.

3. Aluminum bromide plus chlorine yield aluminum chloride and bromine.

4. Hydrochloric acid plus sodium hydroxide yield sodium chloride plus water.

5. Iron plus lead (II) sulfate react forming iron (II) sulfate plus lead.

6. Potassium chlorate when heated produces potassium chloride plus oxygen gas.

7. Sulfuric acid decomposes to form sulfur trioxide gas plus water.

8. Sodium oxide combines with water to make sodium hydroxide.

9. Potassium iodide reacts with bromine forming potassium bromide plus iodine.

10. Sodium phosphate reacts with calcium nitrate to produce sodium nitrate plus calcium phosphate.

Classifying Chemical Reactions

Classify the following reactions as synthesis, decomposition, single replacement or double replacement.

1. $2KClO_3 \rightarrow 2KCl + 3O_2$

2. $HCl + NaOH \rightarrow NaCl + H_2O$

3. $Mg + 2HCl \rightarrow MgCl_2 + H_2$

4. $2H_2 + O_2 \rightarrow 2H_2O$

5. $2Al + 3NiBr_2 \rightarrow 2AlBr_3 + 3Ni$

6. $4Al + 3O_2 \rightarrow 2Al_2O_3$

7. $2NaCl \rightarrow 2Na + Cl_2$

8. $CaCl_2 + F_2 \rightarrow CaF_2 + Cl_2$

9. $AgNO_3 + KCl \rightarrow AgCl + KNO_3$

10. $N_2 + 3H_2 \rightarrow 2NH_3$

11. $2H_2O_2 \rightarrow 2H_2O + O_2$

12. $(NH_4)_2SO_4 + Ba(NO_3)_2 \rightarrow BaSO_4 + 2NH_4NO_3$

13. $MgI_2 + Br_2 \rightarrow MgBr_2 + I_2$

14. $SO_3 + H_2O \rightarrow H_2SO_4$

15. $6KCl + Zn_3(PO_4)_2 \rightarrow 3ZnCl_2 + 2K_3PO_4$

45   ©Instructional Fair, Inc.

Conservation of Mass

In chemical reactions, mass is neither gained nor lost. The total mass of all the reactants equals the total mass of all the products. Atoms are just rearranged into different compounds. Using this idea, solve the following problems.

1. $2KClO_3 \rightarrow 2KCl + 3O_2$
    If 500 g of $KClO_3$ decomposes and produces 303 g of KCl, how many grams of O_2 are produced?

    _____

2. $N_2 + 3H_2 \rightarrow 2NH_3$
    How many grams of H_2 are needed to react with 100 g of N_2 to produce 121 g of NH_3?

    _____

3. $4Fe + 3O_2 \rightarrow 2Fe_2O_3$
    How many grams of oxygen are needed to react with 350 g of iron to produce 500 g of Fe_2O_3?

    _____

4. $CH_4 + 2O_2 \rightarrow CO_2 + 2H_2O$
    16 g of CH_4 react with 64 g of O_2, producing 44 g of CO_2. How many grams of water are produced?

    _____

5. $CaCO_3 \rightarrow CaO + CO_2$
    How much CO_2 is produced from the decomposition of 200 g of $CaCO_3$ if 112 g of CaO are produced?

    _____

Acid, Base or Salt

Classify each of the following compounds as an acid, base or salt. Then, indicate whether each acid and base is strong or weak.

1. HNO_3 _____ _____

2. $NaOH$ _____ _____

3. $NaNO_3$ _____ _____

4. HCl _____ _____

5. KCl _____ _____

6. $Ba(OH)_2$ _____ _____

7. KOH _____ _____

8. H_2S _____ _____

9. $Al(NO_3)_3$ _____ _____

10. H_2SO_4 _____ _____

11. $CaCl_2$ _____ _____

12. H_3PO_4 _____ _____

13. Na_2SO_4 _____ _____

14. $Mg(OH)_2$ _____ _____

15. H_2CO_3 _____ _____

16. NH_4OH _____ _____

17. NH_4Cl _____ _____

18. HBr _____ _____

19. $FeBr_3$ _____ _____

20. HF _____ _____

pH

pH is a scale that measures the hydronium ion concentration of a solution. Therefore, the pH scale can be used to determine the acidity of a solution. A pH of less than 7 indicates an acidic solution, a pH of 7 is neutral, and a pH of greater than 7 up to 14 is basic. The lower the pH, the higher the acidity. The higher the pH, the lower the acidity.

Indicators are substances that change color at a different pH levels. Phenolphthalein is colorless in an acid and a neutral solution, pink in a base. Blue litmus changes to red in an acid, and remains blue in neutral and basic solutions. Red litmus remains red in acidic and neutral substances, but turns blue in bases.

Complete the following chart.

pH	Acid, Base, Neutral	Phenolphthalein	Blue Litmus	Red Litmus
2				
8				
4				
7				
13				
11				
5				
1				

pH of Salt Solutions

A salt is formed from the reaction of an acid and a base.

A strong acid + a strong base → neutral salt

A strong acid + a weak base → acidic salt

A weak acid + a strong base → basic salt

The salt of a weak acid and a weak base may be acidic, neutral or basic, depending on the relative strengths of the acids and bases involved.

The strong acids are HI, HBr, HCl, HNO_3, H_2SO_4 and $HClO_4$. The strong bases are the Group I and Group II hydroxides. Most others are considered weak.

Complete the following chart. The first one is done for you.

Salt	Parent Acid	Acid Strength	Parent Base	Base Strength	Type of Salt
1. KBr	HBr	Strong	KOH	Strong	Neutral
2. $Fe(NO_3)_2$					
3. NaF					
4. NH_4Cl					
5. $Ca(NO_3)_2$					
6. Li_3PO_4					
7. K_2SO_4					
8. AlI_3					
9. $MgCO_3$					
10. $Zn(ClO_4)_2$					

Conductors and Electrolytes

Pure metals are good conductors of electricity. Electrolytes are aqueous solutions that conduct electricity. Acids, bases and salts (ionic compounds) are electrolytes. Nonelectrolytes are aqueous solutions that do not conduct electricity. The solutes used to form nonelectrolytes are covalently bonded.

Classify the following as conductors or nonconductors by writing C or N next to each.

1. copper _____

2. hydrogen _____

3. NaOH(aq) _____

4. NaCl(s) _____

5. NaCl(aq) _____

6. magnesium _____

7. H_2SO_4 _____

8. NH_4OH _____

9. HCl(aq) _____

10. $Ca(OH)_2$(aq) _____

11. $C_6H_{12}O_6$(aq) _____

12. CH_3OH _____

13. KNO_3(s) _____

14. KNO_3(aq) _____

15. chlorine _____

16. HNO_3 _____

17. $NaNO_3$(aq) _____

18. $C_{12}H_{22}O_{11}$ _____

19. C_2H_5OH _____

20. gold _____

Concentration (Mass/Volume)

> Concentration = $\dfrac{\text{mass of solute}}{\text{volume of solution}}$

Solve the following problems.

1. A sugar solution contains 26 g of sugar in 0.50 L of solution. What is the concentration in g/L?

   _____

2. 45 grams of salt are dissolved in 0.10 L of solution. What is the concentration in g/L?

   _____

3. A solution contains 25 g of sugar per liter of solution. How many grams of sugar are in 1.5 L of solution?

   _____

4. A solution contains 85 g of corn syrup per liter of solution. How many grams of corn syrup are in 500 mL of solution?

   _____

5. How many liters of salt solution would be needed to provide 30 g of salt if the concentration of the solution is 20 g/L?

   _____

Concentration (% by Volume)

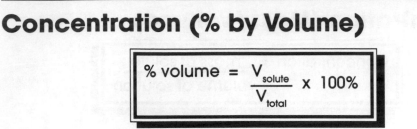

$$\% \text{ volume } = \frac{V_{solute}}{V_{total}} \times 100\%$$

Solve the following problems. Assume all volumes are additive.

1. 25 mL of ethanol is added to enough water to make 100 mL of solution. Find the percent by volume of ethanol.

_____

2. 50 mL of ethanol is added to 50 mL of water. What is the percent by volume of ethanol?

_____

3. 3.0 liters of antifreeze is added to 4.0 liters of water. Find the percent by volume of antifreeze.

_____

4. A popular fruit drink contains 5% by volume fruit juice. How much fruit juice is in 500 mL of the fruit drink?

_____

5. How much corn syrup should be added to water to make 200 mL of a 10% by volume solution?

_____

Concentration (% by Mass)

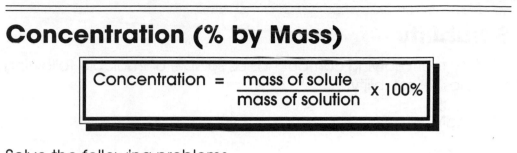

$$\text{Concentration} = \frac{\text{mass of solute}}{\text{mass of solution}} \times 100\%$$

Solve the following problems.

1. 25 g of sugar in 75 g of solution will have what percent by mass of sugar?

    _____

2. 35 g of salt is dissolved in 500 g of total solution. What is the percent by mass of salt?

    _____

3. 50 g of sugar are dissolved in 50 g of water. What is the percent by mass of sugar?

    _____

4. 75 g of potassium nitrate are dissolved in 150 g of water. What is the percent by mass of potassium nitrate?

    _____

5. How many grams of sodium bromide are in 200 g of a solution that is 15% sodium bromide by mass?

    _____

Solubility

Classify the following compounds as soluble or insoluble following the rules for solubility.

1. $AgNO_3$ _____

2. K_2CO_3 _____

3. $Ca_3(PO_4)_2$ _____

4. $AgCl$ _____

5. $NaOH$ _____

6. NH_4Cl _____

7. KBr _____

8. $MgCO_3$ _____

9. FeS _____

10. $CuC_2H_3O_2$ _____

11. $(NH_4)_2SO_4$ _____

12. $Ca(OH)_2$ _____

13. Na_2SO_4 _____

14. $BaSO_4$ _____

15. KI _____

16. $(NH_4)_3PO_4$ _____

17. $Cu(NO_3)_2$ _____

18. $AlPO_4$ _____

19. $CaCO_3$ _____

20. $(NH_4)_2S$ _____

Naming Organic Compounds

Name the following organic compounds.

1.

$$H - \underset{\underset{\displaystyle H}{|}}{\overset{\overset{\displaystyle H}{|}}{C}} - H$$

5.

$$H - \overset{\overset{\displaystyle H}{|}}{C} = \overset{\overset{\displaystyle H}{|}}{C} - \underset{\underset{\displaystyle H}{|}}{\overset{\overset{\displaystyle H}{|}}{C}} - \underset{\underset{\displaystyle H}{|}}{\overset{\overset{\displaystyle H}{|}}{C}} - H$$

2.

$$H - \overset{\overset{\displaystyle H}{|}}{C} = \overset{\overset{\displaystyle H}{|}}{C} - \underset{\underset{\displaystyle H}{|}}{\overset{\overset{\displaystyle H}{|}}{C}} - H$$

6.

$$H - \underset{\underset{\displaystyle H}{|}}{\overset{\overset{\displaystyle H}{|}}{C}} - \underset{\underset{\displaystyle H}{|}}{\overset{\overset{\displaystyle H}{|}}{C}} - \underset{\underset{\displaystyle H}{|}}{\overset{\overset{\displaystyle H}{|}}{C}} - H$$

3.

$$H - C \equiv C - H$$

7.

$$H - C \equiv C - \underset{\underset{\displaystyle H}{|}}{\overset{\overset{\displaystyle H}{|}}{C}} - H$$

4.

$$H - \underset{\underset{\displaystyle H}{|}}{\overset{\overset{\displaystyle H}{|}}{C}} - \underset{\underset{\displaystyle H}{|}}{\overset{\overset{\displaystyle H}{|}}{C}} - H$$

8.

$$H - \overset{\overset{\displaystyle H}{|}}{C} = \overset{\overset{\displaystyle H}{|}}{C} - H$$

Drawing Structural Formulas

Draw the structural formula of the following compounds.

1. ethane

2. propene

3. 1-butyne

4. ethene

5. propyne

6. methane

7. ethyne

8. 1-pentene

56

Isomers

Isomers have the same chemical formula but different structural formulas. Match the structure in Column I with its isomer in Column II.

Column I

1.

$$H - \overset{\displaystyle \overset{H}{|}}{\underset{\displaystyle \underset{H}{|}}{C}} - \overset{\displaystyle \overset{H}{|}}{\underset{\displaystyle \underset{H}{|}}{C}} - \overset{\displaystyle \overset{H}{|}}{\underset{\displaystyle \underset{H}{|}}{C}} - OH$$

_____

2.

$$H - \overset{\displaystyle \overset{H}{|}}{\underset{\displaystyle \underset{H}{|}}{C}} - \overset{\displaystyle \overset{O}{\|}}{C} - \overset{\displaystyle \overset{H}{|}}{\underset{\displaystyle \underset{H}{|}}{C}} - H$$

_____

3.

$$H - \overset{\displaystyle \overset{H}{|}}{\underset{\displaystyle \underset{H}{|}}{C}} - \overset{\displaystyle \overset{H}{|}}{\underset{\displaystyle \underset{H}{|}}{C}} - \overset{\displaystyle \overset{H}{|}}{\underset{\displaystyle \underset{H}{|}}{C}} - \overset{\displaystyle \overset{H}{|}}{\underset{\displaystyle \underset{H}{|}}{C}} - H$$

_____

4.

$$H - \overset{\displaystyle \overset{H}{|}}{\underset{\displaystyle \underset{H}{|}}{C}} - \overset{\displaystyle \overset{H}{|}}{\underset{\displaystyle \underset{H}{|}}{C}} - \overset{\displaystyle \overset{H}{|}}{\underset{\displaystyle \underset{H}{|}}{C}} - \overset{\displaystyle \overset{H}{|}}{\underset{\displaystyle \underset{H}{|}}{C}} - \overset{\displaystyle \overset{H}{|}}{\underset{\displaystyle \underset{H}{|}}{C}} - H$$

_____

5.

$$H - \overset{\displaystyle \overset{H}{|}}{\underset{\displaystyle \underset{H}{|}}{C}} - \overset{\displaystyle \overset{O}{\|}}{C} - OH$$

_____

Column II

a)

$$H - \overset{\displaystyle \overset{H}{|}}{\underset{\displaystyle \underset{H}{|}}{C}} - \overset{\displaystyle \overset{CH_3}{|}}{\underset{\displaystyle \underset{H}{|}}{C}} - \overset{\displaystyle \overset{H}{|}}{\underset{\displaystyle \underset{H}{|}}{C}} - H$$

b)

$$H - \overset{\displaystyle \overset{H}{|}}{\underset{\displaystyle \underset{H}{|}}{C}} - \overset{\displaystyle \overset{OH}{|}}{\underset{\displaystyle \underset{H}{|}}{C}} - \overset{\displaystyle \overset{H}{|}}{\underset{\displaystyle \underset{H}{|}}{C}} - H$$

c)

$$H_3C - \overset{\displaystyle \overset{CH_3}{|}}{\underset{\displaystyle \underset{CH_3}{|}}{C}} - CH_3$$

d)

$$H - \overset{\displaystyle \overset{H}{|}}{\underset{\displaystyle \underset{H}{|}}{C}} - \overset{\displaystyle \overset{H}{|}}{\underset{\displaystyle \underset{H}{|}}{C}} - \overset{\displaystyle \overset{O}{\|}}{C} - H$$

e)

$$H - \overset{\displaystyle \overset{H}{|}}{\underset{\displaystyle \underset{H}{|}}{C}} - O - \overset{\displaystyle \overset{O}{\|}}{C} - H$$

Wave Diagram

On the following diagram, place the following terms in their correct places: amplitude, wavelength, crest, trough, rest position.

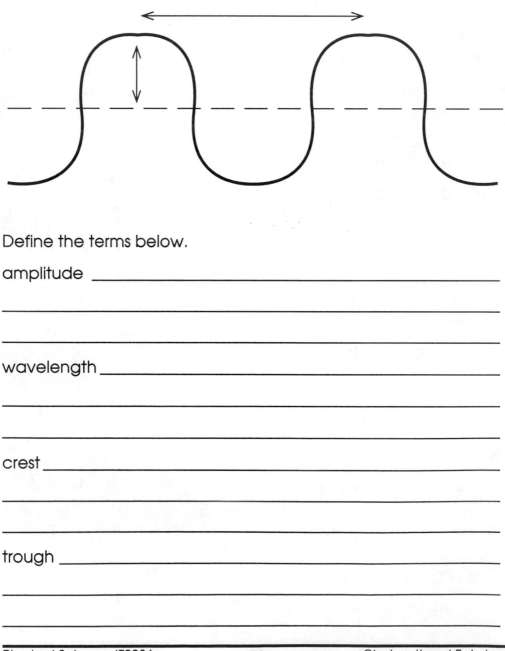

Define the terms below.

amplitude _____
_____
_____

wavelength _____
_____
_____

crest _____
_____
_____

trough _____
_____
_____

Wave Velocity Calculations

Velocity = Wavelength x Frequency

Solve the following problems.

1. A tuning fork has a frequency of 280 hertz, and the wavelength of the sound produced is 1.5 meters. Calculate the velocity of the wave.

   _____

2. A wave is moving toward shore with a velocity of 5.0 m/s. If its frequency is 2.5 hertz, what is its wavelength?

   _____

3. The speed of light is 3.0×10^8 m/s. Red light has a wavelength of 7×10^{-7} m. What is its frequency?

   _____

4. The frequency of violet light is 7.5×10^{14} hertz. What is its wavelength?

   _____

5. A jump rope is shaken producing a wave with a wavelength of 0.5 m with the crest of the wave passing a certain point 4 times per second. What is the velocity of the wave?

   _____

Reflection

Draw the expected path of the light rays as they reflect off the following plane mirrors.

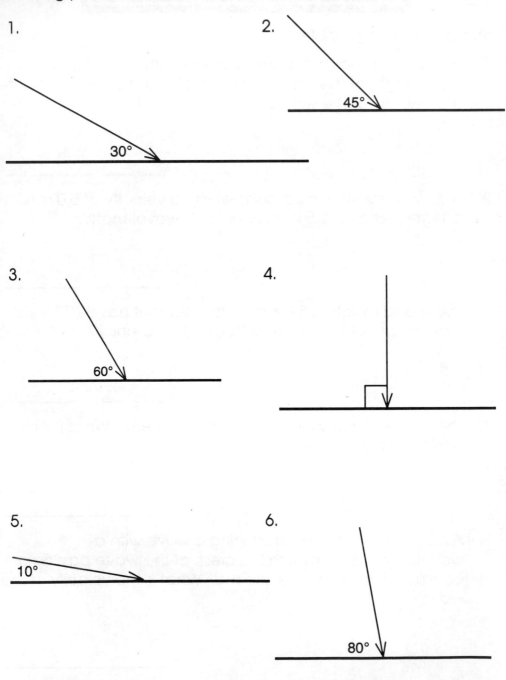

1.

30°

2.

45°

3.

60°

4.

5.

10°

6.

80°

Refraction

Draw the pathway of the light beam as it passes through each of the following substances. Using a protractor, measure the refracted angle.

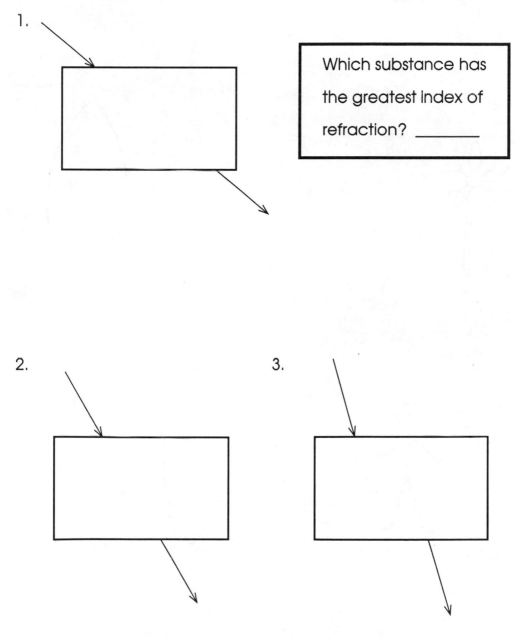

Which substance has the greatest index of refraction? _____

Light Rays and Convex Lenses

Draw the pathways of the light from the objects on the left through the convex lenses. Label the focal point and the inverted image.

Light Rays and Concave Lenses

Draw the path of light through the concave lenses below. Label the image and focal point.

White Light Spectrum

Label the colors coming through this prism as the white light is reflected through it.

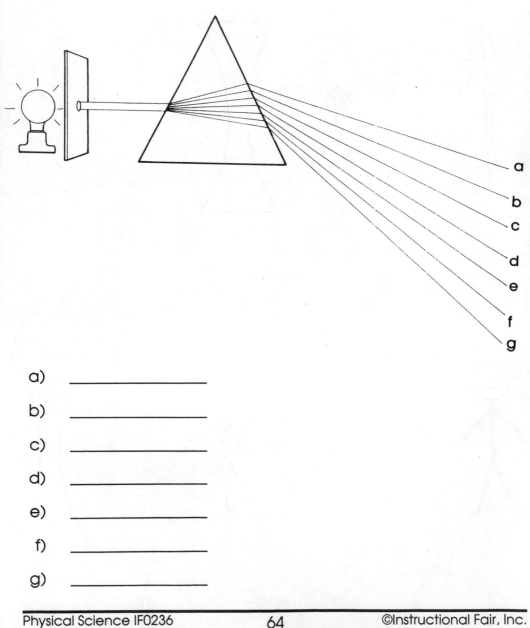

a) _____

b) _____

c) _____

d) _____

e) _____

f) _____

g) _____

Light Matching

Match the definition or corresponding phrase in Column II with the correct word in Column I.

I		II
1. hertz _____		a) the angle at which a ray "bounces off" a surface
2. wave velocity _____		b) bending of light waves when they pass through another substance
3. frequency _____		
4. reflection _____		c) an imaginary line drawn at a right angle to the surface of a barrier
5. wavelength _____		d) number of waves that pass a given point in one second
6. refraction _____		e) tells how much a ray of light will bend as it travels through a given material
7. crest _____		
8. trough _____		f) translucent material that separates white light into colors
9. photon _____		g) frequency times wavelength
		h) lowest part of a wave
10. light _____		i) type of electromagnetic radiation
11. prism _____		j) unit for frequency
12. index of refraction _____		k) the bouncing of a wave off another object
13. angle of incidence _____		l) a continuous band of colors arranged according to wavelength or frequency
14. angle of reflection _____		m) distance between corresponding points on two waves
15. visible light spectrum _____		
		n) particle of light
16. normal _____		o) highest point of a wave
		p) the angle at which a ray of light strikes a surface

Magnetic Fields

Draw the pattern of magnetic fields around these magnets.

N   S

N   S

N   N

Calculating Current

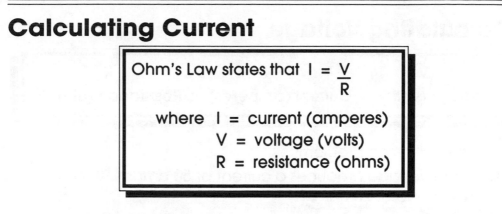

Ohm's Law states that $I = \dfrac{V}{R}$

where I = current (amperes)
V = voltage (volts)
R = resistance (ohms)

Solve the following problems.

1. What is the current produced with a 9-volt battery through a resistance of 100 ohms?

_____

2. Find the current when a 12-volt battery is connected through a resistance of 25 ohms.

_____

3. If the potential difference is 120 volts and the resistance is 50 ohms, what is the current?

_____

4. What would be the current in Problem 3 if the potential difference were doubled?

_____

5. What would be the current in Problem 3 if the resistance were doubled?

_____

Calculating Voltage

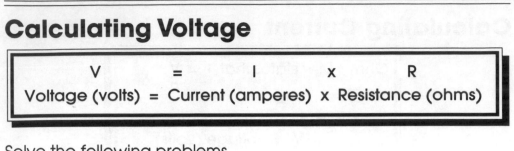

$$V \qquad = \qquad I \qquad x \qquad R$$

Voltage (volts) = Current (amperes) x Resistance (ohms)

Solve the following problems.

1. What voltage produces a current of 50 amps with a resistance of 20 ohms?

   _____

2. Silver has a resistance of 1.98×10^{-4} ohms. What voltage would produce a current of 100 amps?

   _____

3. A current of 250 amps is flowing through a copper wire with a resistance of 2.09×10^{-4} ohms. What is the voltage?

   _____

4. What voltage produces a current of 500 amps with a resistance of 50 ohms?

   _____

5. What voltage would produce a current of 100 amps through an aluminum wire which has a resistance of 3.44×10^{-4} ohms?

   _____

Calculating Resistance

$$R = \frac{V}{I} \qquad \text{Resistance (ohms)} = \frac{\text{Voltage (volts)}}{\text{Current (amperes)}}$$

Solve the following problems.

1. What resistance would produce a current of 200 amperes with a potential difference of 2,000 volts?

   _____

2. A 12-volt battery produces a current of 25 amperes. What is the resistance?

   _____

3. A 9-volt battery produces a current of 2.0 amperes. What is the resistance?

   _____

4. An overhead wire has a potential difference of 2,000 volts. If the current flowing through the wire is one million amperes, what is the resistance of the wire?

   _____

5. What is the resistance of a light bulb if a 120-volt potential difference produces a current of 0.8 amperes?

   _____

Ohm's Law Problems

Using Ohm's Law, solve the following problems.

1. What is the current produced by a potential difference of 240 volts through a resistance of 0.2 ohms?

   _____

2. What resistance would produce a current of 120 amps from a 6-volt battery?

   _____

3. What voltage is necessary to produce a current of 200 amperes through a resistance of 1×10^{-3} ohms?

   _____

4. What is the current produced by a 9-volt battery flowing through a resistance of 2×10^{-4} ohms?

   _____

5. What is the potential difference if a resistance of 25 ohms produces a current of 250 amperes?

   _____

Calculating Power

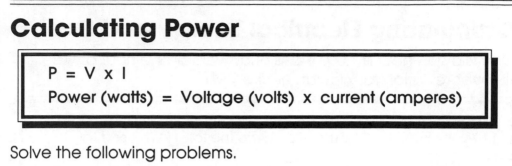

P = V x I
Power (watts) = Voltage (volts) x current (amperes)

Solve the following problems.

1. A 6-volt battery produces a current of 0.5 amps. What is the power in the circuit?

   _____

2. A 100-watt light bulb is operating on 1.2 amperes current. What is the voltage?

   _____

3. A potential difference of 120 volts is operating on a 500-watt microwave oven. What is the current being used?

   _____

4. A light bulb uses 0.625 amperes from a source of 120 volts. How much power is used by the bulb?

   _____

5. What voltage is necessary to run a 500-watt motor with a current of 200 amperes?

   _____

Calculating Electrical Energy and Cost

One kilowatt hour is 1,000 watts of power for one hour of time. The abbreviation for kilowatt hour is kWh.

Example: A coffee pot operates on 2 amperes of current on a 110-volt circuit for 3 hours. Calculate the total kWh used.

1. Determine power:
$$P = V \times I$$
$$= 110 \text{ volts} \times 2 \text{ amps}$$
$$= 220 \text{ watts}$$

2. Convert watts to kilowatts:
$$220 \text{ watts} \times \frac{1 \text{ kilowatt}}{1,000 \text{ watts}} = 0.22 \text{ kW}$$

$$kWh = P \times hours$$
$$kWh = \frac{V \times I \times hours}{1,000}$$

3. Multiply by the hours given in the problem:
$$0.22 \text{ kW} \times 3 \text{ hrs} = 0.66 \text{ kWh}$$

Solve the following problems.

1. A microwave oven operates on 5 amps of current on a 110-volt circuit for one hour. Calculate the total kilowatt hours used. _____

2. How much would it cost to run the microwave in Problem 1 if the cost of energy is $0.10 per kWh? _____

3. An electric stove operates on 20 amps of current on a 220-volt circuit for one hour. Calculate the total kilowatt hours used. _____

4. What is the cost of using the stove in Problem 3 if the cost of energy if $0.10 per kWh? _____

5. A refrigerator operates on 15 amps of current on a 220-volt circuit for 18 hours per day. How many kilowatt hours are used per day? _____

6. If the electric costs are 15¢ per kWh, how much does it cost to run the refrigerator in Problem 5 per day? _____

Series and Parallel Circuits

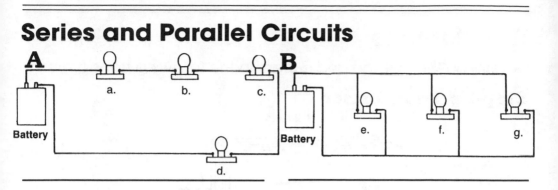

Answer the following questions regarding circuits A and B above.

1. Label circuits A and B as series or parallel.
2. If bulb a burns out, will bulb d still light? _____
3. If bulb f burns out, will bulb g still light? _____
4. If bulbs b, c and d are burned out, will bulb a still light?
   _____
5. If bulbs f and g are missing, will bulb c still light?
   _____
6. Draw a diagram of a parallel circuit having 3 light bulbs,
   3 switches and a battery. Each light bulb is on a separate
   switch.

7. Draw a diagram of a series circuit having 3 light bulbs, one
   switch and a battery.

8. Would series or parallel circuits be better for wiring light in a
   house? _____
   Why? _____

   _____

Transformers

Determine the voltage and current in the following transformers.

Step-Up Transformer

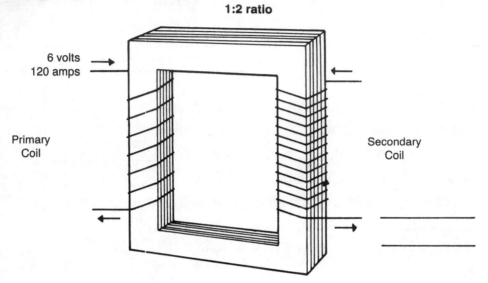

1:2 ratio

6 volts
120 amps →

Primary
Coil

Secondary
Coil

_____

_____

Step-Down Transformer

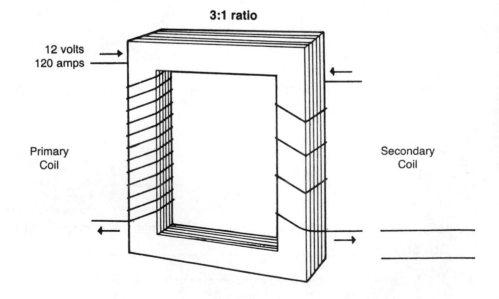

3:1 ratio

12 volts
120 amps →

Primary
Coil

Secondary
Coil

_____

_____

Half-life Calculations

Half-life is the time required for one-half of a radioactive nuclide to decay (change to another element). It is possible to calculate the amount of a radioactive element that will be left if we know its half-life.

Example: The half-life of Po-214 is 0.001 second. How much of a 10 g sample will be left after 0.003 seconds?

Answer: Calculate the number of half-lives:

$$0.003 \text{ seconds} \times \frac{1 \text{ half-life}}{0.001 \text{ second}} = 3 \text{ half-lives}$$

After 0 half-lives, 10 g are left.
After 1 half-life, 5 g are left.
After 2 half-lives, 2.5 g are left.
After 3 half-lives, 1.25 g are left.

Solve the following problems.

1. The half-life of radon-222 is 3.8 days. How much of a 100 g sample is left after 15.2 days? _____

2. Carbon-14 has a half-life of 5,730 years. If a sample contains 70 mg originally, how much is left after 17,190 years? _____

3. How much of a 500 g sample of potassium-42 is left after 62 hours? The half-life of K-42 is 12.4 hours?

   _____

4. The half-life of cobalt-60 is 5.26 years. If 50 g are left after 15.8 years, how many grams were in the original sample?

   _____

5. The half-life of I-131 is 8.07 days. If 25 g are left after 40.35 days, how many grams were in the original sample?

   _____

6. If 100 g of Au-198 decays to 6.25 g in 10.8 days, what is the half-life of Au-198? _____

2. 1. 1.96×10^{-3} g/mL; 2. 1.0 g/cm³;
   3. 5.0 g/mL; 4. 8.96 g/cm³; 5. gold;
   6. benzene; 7. 7.8 g/cm³

3. 1. 50 km/hr; 2. 600 mi/hr;
   3. 5.3 km/hr; 4. 420 mi; 5. 3.6 hrs;
   6. 7.5 hrs; 7. 3,000 km; 8. 12 km

4.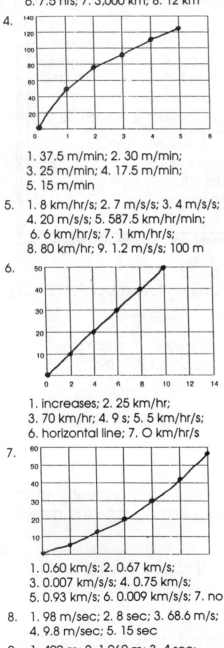

   1. 37.5 m/min; 2. 30 m/min;
   3. 25 m/min; 4. 17.5 m/min;
   5. 15 m/min

5. 1. 8 km/hr/s; 2. 7 m/s/s; 3. 4 m/s/s;
   4. 20 m/s/s; 5. 587.5 km/hr/min;
   6. 6 km/hr/s; 7. 1 km/hr/s;
   8. 80 km/hr; 9. 1.2 m/s/s; 100 m

6. 1. increases; 2. 25 km/hr;
   3. 70 km/hr; 4. 9 s; 5. 5 km/hr/s;
   6. horizontal line; 7. 0 km/hr/s

7. 1. 0.60 km/s; 2. 0.67 km/s;
   3. 0.007 km/s; 4. 0.75 km/s;
   5. 0.93 km/s; 6. 0.009 km/s/s; 7. no

8. 1. 98 m/sec; 2. 8 sec; 3. 68.6 m/s;
   4. 9.8 m/sec; 5. 15 sec

9. 1. 490 m; 2. 1,960 m; 3. 4 sec;
   4. 98 m/s; 5. 49 m/s; 6. 80 sec;
   7. 784 m/s; 8. 392 m/s

10.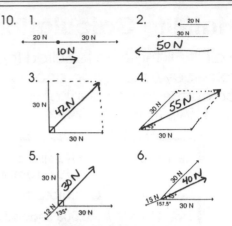

11. 1. 6,000 N; 2. 30 N; 3. 15 kg;
    4. 50 m/s²; 5. 2,800 kg

12. 1. g; j; a; d; e; b; k; h; c; i; f

13. 1. 5,000 cal; 2. 21,000 joules;
    3. 1,840 joules; 4. 0.21 cal/g C°;
    5. 10° C

14. 1. 170,000 J or 1.7×10^5 J;
    2. 170 kilojoules; 3. 1,150,000 J or
    1.15×10^6 J; 4. 15 g; 5. 25 g

15. 1. pulley; 2. lever; 3. inclined plane;
    4. wedge; 5. wheel and axle;
    6. lever; 7. inclined plane; 8. screw;
    9. lever; 10. wheel and axle

16. 1. first class; 2. second class; 3. third
    class; 4. first class; 5. first class;
    6. third class; 7. second class;
    8. second class

17. 1. 30,000 joules; 2. 63 joules;
    3. potential, 90 joules; 4. 30 joules;
    5. 60 joules; 6. kinetic, 6×10^6 joules

18. 1. 2 joules; 2. 45 joules;
    3. 10 newtons; 4. 1.5 meters;
    5. 2,000 joules; 6. 0 joules

19. 1. MA = 3; 2. MA = 4; 3. MA = 4;
    4. MA = 1; 5. MA = 5; 6. MA = 2;
    7. MA = 2; 8. MA = 3

20. 1. 80%; 2. 45%; 3. 67%; 4. 72%;
    5. 83%; 6. 80 J

21. 1. 50 watts; 2. 70 watts; 3. 250 watts;
    4. 150,000 joules; 5. 216,000 joules

22. 1. S; 2. S; 3. M; 4. M; 5. S; 6. S; 7. S;
    8. M; 9. M; 10. M; 11. S; 12. M; 13. M;
    14. S; 15. M; 16. M; 17. S; 18. M;
    19. M; 20. M

23. 1. homogeneous; 2. heterogeneous;
3. heterogeneous; 4. homogeneous;
5. heterogeneous; 6. homogeneous;
7. homogeneous; 8. homogeneous;
9. heterogenous;
10. heterogeneous;
11. homogeneous;
12. homogeneous;
13. heterogeneous;
14. homogeneous;
15. heterogeneous

24. 1. physical; 2. physical; 3. chemical;
4. physical; 5. chemical;
6. chemical; 7. physical; 8. physical;
9. chemical; 10. chemical;
11. physical; 12. physical;
13. chemical

25. 1. physical; 2. chemical; 3. physical;
4. physical; 5. chemical;
6. chemical; 7. physical;
8. chemical; 9. chemical;
10. chemical

26. 1. O; 2. H; 3. Cl; 4. Na; 5. F; 6. C;
7. He; 8. N; 9. Cu; 10. S; 11. Mg;
12. Mn; 13. Ne; 14. Br; 15. P; 16. Ag;
17. Pb; 18. Fe; 19. Ca; 20. K;
21. copper; 22. potassium;
23. carbon; 24. gold; 25. zinc;
26. lead; 27. iron; 28. sodium;
29. sulfur; 30. aluminum;
31. calcium; 32. silver; 33.
phosphorus; 34. oxygen; 35. iodine;
36. tin; 37. hydrogen; 38. fluorine;
39. nickel; 40. mercury

27. 1. 12, 24, 0, 12, 12, 12; 2. 19, 39, 0,
19, 20, 19; 3. 11, 23, +1, 11, 12, 10;
4. 9, 19, -1, 9, 10, 10; 5. 13, 27, +3, 13,
14, 10; 6. 1, 1, 0, 1, 0, 1; 7. 12, 24, +2,
12, 12, 10; 8. 47, 108, 0, 47, 61, 47;
9. 16, 32, -2, 16, 16, 18; 10. 1, 2, 0, 1,
1, 1; 11. 17, 35, -1, 17, 18, 18; 12. 4, 9,
+2, 4, 5, 2

28. 1.   2.

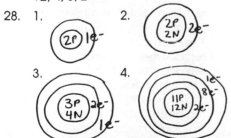

3.   4.

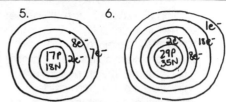

5.   6.

29. 1. metal; 2. metal; 3. nonmetal;
4. nonmetal; 5. metal; 6. nonmetal;
7. metal; 8. metal; 9. nonmetal;
10. metal; 11. nonmetal;
12. nonmetal; 13. nonmetal;
14. metal; 15. nonmetal

30. 1. Na; 2. F_2; 3. N_2; 4. Rb; 5. Ca; 6. K;
7. O_2; 8. Br_2; 9. Na; 10. S; 11. O_2;
12. Cl_2; 13. Fr; 14. Rb; 15. Be; 16. Cl_2;
17. I_2; 18. Ra; 19. Sr; 20. K; 21. Mg; 22.
S; 23. U; 24. Br_2; 25. F_2; 26. Rb;
27. Ra; 28. Na; 29. I_2; 30. Ca

31. 1. C; 2. F; 3. A; 4. H; 5. B; 6. D; 7. G;
8. E; 9. J; 10. I

32. 1. ionic; 2. covalent; 3. covalent;
4. both; 5. ionic; 6. ionic; 7. both;
8. covalent; 9. covalent; 10. ionic;
11. ionic; 12. both; 13. covalent; 14.
ionic; 15. both; 16. covalent;
17. both; 18. ionic; 19. covalent;
20. covalent

33. 1. 2; 2. 7; 3. 5; 4. 3; 5. 8; 6. 5; 7. 6;
8. 13; 9. 17; 10. 9; 11. 9; 12. 6; 13. 4;
14. 8; 15. 20; 16. 5; 17. 8; 18. 15;
19. 4; 20. 6

34. 1. 58 g; 2. 98 g; 3. 101 g; 4. 110 g;
5. 30 g; 6. 171 g; 7. 98 g; 8. 310 g;
9. 342 g; 10. 148 g; 11. 188 g;
12. 158 g; 13. 34 g; 14. 98 g;
15. 149 g; 16. 160 g; 17. 82 g;
18. 142 g; 19. 472 g; 20. 158 g

35. 1. 27%; 2. 6.8 g; 3. 40%; 4. 30 g;
5. 39%; 6. 1.95 g; 7. 64%. 8. 80 g;
9. 65%; 10. 22.8 g

36. 1. NaCl; 2. BaF_2; 3. K_2S; 4. LiBr; 5. AlI_3;
6. ZnS; 7. Ag_2O; 8. Mg_3P_2; 9. NiO;
10. Ni_2O_3; 11. FeO; 12. Fe_2O_3; 13. CrS;
14. Cr_2S_3; 15. CuCl; 16. $CuCl_2$;
17. PbO; 18. PbO_2; 19. $MnBr_2$;
20. $MnBr_4$

37. 1. barium chloride; 2. sodium
fluoride; 3. silver oxide; 4. copper (I)
bromide; 5. copper (II) bromide;

6. iron (II) oxide; 7. iron (III) oxide;
8. magnesium sulfide; 9. aluminum
oxide; 10. calcium iodide;
11. potassium sulfide; 12. chromium
(II) chloride; 13. chromium (III)
chloride; 14. calcium oxide;
15. barium phosphide; 16. mercury
(I) iodide; 17. sodium oxide;
18. beryllium sulfide;
19. manganese (II) oxide;
20. manganese (III) oxide

38. 1. carbon monoxide; 2. carbon
dioxide; 3. sulfur dioxide; 4. nitrogen
dioxide; 5. dinitrogen monoxide;
6. sulfur trioxide; 7. carbon
tetrachloride; 8. nitrogen
monoxide; 9. dinitrogen pentoxide;
10. diphosphorus pentoxide;
11. dinitrogen tetroxide; 12. carbon
disulfide; 13. oxygen difluoride;
14. phosphorus trichloride;
15. phosphorus pentabromide

39. 2. $NaOH$, $NaNO_3$, Na_2CO_3, Na_2SO_4,
Na_3PO_4; 3. $Mg(OH)_2$, $Mg(NO_3)_2$,
$MgCO_3$, $MgSO_4$, $Mg_3(PO_4)_2$;
4. NH_4OH, NH_4NO_3, $(NH_4)_2SO_4$,
$(NH_4)_3PO_4$; 5. $Ca(OH)_2$, $Ca(NO_3)_3$,
$CaCO_3$, $CaSO_4$, $Ca_3(PO_4)_2$; 6. KOH,
KNO_3, K_2CO_3, K_2SO_4, K_3PO_4;
7. $Al(OH)_3$, $Al(NO_3)_2$, $Al_2(CO_3)_3$,
$Al_2(SO_4)_3$, $AlPO_4$; 8. $Pb(OH)_4$,
$Pb(NO_3)_4$, $Pb(CO_3)_2$, $Pb(SO_4)_2$,
$Pb_3(PO_4)_4$

40. 1. sodium nitrate; 2. calcium
hydroxide; 3. potassium carbonate;
4. ammonium chloride;
5. magnesium sulfate; 6. aluminum
phosphate; 7. ammonium sulfate;
8. sodium phosphate; 9. copper (II)
sulfate; 10. ammonium hydroxide;
11. lithium sulfite; 12. magnesium
nitrate; 13. aluminum hydroxide;
14. ammonium phosphate;
15. potassium hydroxide;
16. calcium nitrate; 17. potassium
sulfate; 18. lead (II) hydroxide;
19. sodium peroxide; 20. copper (II)
carbonate

41. 1. sodium chloride; 2. manganese
sulfide; 3. potassium oxide;
4. copper (II) bromide; 5. copper (I)

bromide; 6. carbon dioxide; 7. lead
(II) sulfate; 8. lithium carbonate;
9. sodium carbonate; 10. nitrogen
dioxide; 11. dinitrogen tetroxide;
12. calcium hydroxide;
13. ammonium chloride; 14. sulfur
trioxide; 15. aluminum phosphate;
16. carbon tetrachloride;
17. calcium sulfide; 18. ammonia;
19. magnesium iodide;
20. potassium phosphate

42. 1. CO; 2. $NaCl$; 3. CCl_4; 4. $MgBr_2$;
5. AlI_3; 6. HOH; 7. FeF_2; 8. CO_2;
9. Na_2CO_3; 10. $(NH_4)_2S$; 11. FeO;
12. Fe_2O_3; 13. $MgSO_4$; 14. Na_3PO_4;
15. N_2O_5; 16. PCl_3; 17. $Al_2(SO_3)_3$;
18. Cu_2CO_3; 19. $KHCO_3$; 20. SO_3

43. 1. $CH_4 + 2O_2 \rightarrow CO_2 + 2H_2O$; 2. $2Na$
$+ I_2 \rightarrow 2NaI$; 3. $2N_2 + O_2 \rightarrow 2N_2O$; 4.
$N_2 + 3H_2 \rightarrow 2NH_3$; 5. $2KI + Cl_2 \rightarrow$
$2KCl + I_2$; 6. $2HCl + Ca(OH)_2 \rightarrow$
$CaCl_2 + 2H_2O$; 7. $2KClO_3 \rightarrow 2KCl +$
$3O_2$; 8. $K_3PO_4 + 3HCl \rightarrow 3KCl +$
H_3PO_4; 9. $2S + 3O_2 \rightarrow 2SO_3$; 10. $2KI +$
$Pb(NO_3)_2 \rightarrow 2KNO_3 + PbI_2$;
11. $3CaSO_4 + 2AlBr_3 \rightarrow 3CaBr_2 +$
$Al_2(SO_4)_3$; 12. $2H_2O_2 \rightarrow 2H_2O + O_2$;
13. $2Na + 2H_2O \rightarrow 2NaOH + H_2$;
14. $2C_2H_6 + 7O_2 \rightarrow 4CO_2 + 6H_2O$;
15. $3Mg(NO_3)_2 + 2K_3PO_4 \rightarrow$
$Mg_3(PO_4)_2 + 6KNO_3$

44. 1. $2H_2 + O_2 \rightarrow 2H_2O$; 2. $N_2 + 3H_2 \rightarrow$
$2NH_3$; 3. $2AlBr_3 + 3Cl_2 \rightarrow 2AlCl_3 +$
$3Br_2$; 4. $HCl + NaOH \rightarrow NaCl + H_2O$;
5. $Fe + PbSO_4 \rightarrow FeSO_4 + Pb$;
6. $2KClO_3 \rightarrow 2KCl + 3O_2$; 7. H_2SO_4
$\rightarrow SO_3 + H_2O$ 8. $Na_2O + H_2O \rightarrow$
$2NaOH$; 9. $2KI + Br_2 \rightarrow 2KBr + I_2$; 10.
$2Na_3PO_4 + 3Ca(NO_3)_2 \rightarrow 6NaNO_3 +$
$Ca_3(PO_4)_2$

45. 1. decomposition; 2. double
replacement; 3. single
replacement; 4. synthesis; 5. single
replacement; 6. synthesis;
7. decomposition; 8. single
replacement; 9. double
replacement; 10. synthesis;
11. decomposition; 12. double
replacement; 13. single
replacement; 14. synthesis;
15. double replacement

46. 1. 197 g; 2. 21 g; 3. 150 g; 4. 36 g;
    5. 88 g

47. 1. acid, strong; 2. base, strong;
    3. salt; 4. acid, strong; 5. salt;
    6. base, strong; 7. base, strong;
    8. acid, weak; 9. salt; 10. acid,
    strong; 11. salt; 12. acid, weak;
    13. salt; 14. base, strong; 15. acid,
    weak; 16. base, weak; 17. salt;
    18. acid, strong; 19. salt; 20. acid,
    weak

48. 2—acid, colorless, red, red;
    8—base, pink, blue, blue; 4—acid,
    colorless, red, red; 7—neutral,
    colorless, blue, red; 13—base, pink,
    blue, blue; 11—base, pink, blue,
    blue; 5—acid, colorless, red, red;
    1—acid, colorless, red, red

49. 2. HNO_3, strong, $Fe(OH)_2$, weak,
    acidic; 3. HF, weak, NaOH, strong,
    basic; 4. HCl, strong, NH_4OH, weak,
    acidic; 5. HNO_3, strong, $Ca(OH)_2$,
    strong, neutral; 6. H_3PO_4, weak,
    LiOH, strong, basic; 7. H_2SO_4, strong,
    KOH, strong, neutral; 8. HI, strong,
    $Al(OH)_3$, weak, acidic; 9. H_2CO_3,
    weak, $Mg(OH)_2$, strong, basic;
    10. $HClO_4$, strong, $Zn(OH)_2$, weak,
    acidic

50. 1. C; 2. N; 3. C; 4. N; 5. C; 6. C; 7. C;
    8. C; 9. C; 10. C; 11. N; 12. N; 13. N;
    14. C; 15. N; 16. C; 17. C; 18. N;
    19. N; 20. C

51. 1. 52 g/L; 2. 450 g/L; 3. 37.5 g;
    4. 42.5 g; 5. 1.5 L

52. 1. 25%; 2. 50%; 3. 43%; 4. 25 mL;
    5. 20 mL

53. 1. 33%, 2. 7%; 3. 50%; 4. 33%; 5. 30 g

54. 1. soluble; 2. soluble; 3. insoluble;
    4. insoluble; 5. soluble; 6. soluble;
    7. soluble; 8. insoluble; 9. insoluble;
    10. soluble; 11. soluble; 12. insoluble;
    13. soluble; 14. insoluble; 15. soluble;
    16. soluble; 17. soluble; 18 insoluble;
    19. insoluble; 20. soluble

55. 1. methane; 2. propene; 3. ethyne;
    4. ethane; 5. 1-butene; 6. propane;
    7. propyne; 8. ethene

56.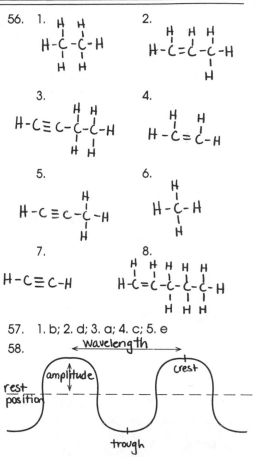

57. 1. b; 2. d; 3. a; 4. c; 5. e

58.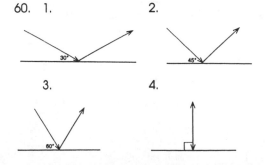

    amplitude—the distance a wave
    rises or falls from its rest position;
    wavelength—the distance from a
    point on one wave to the
    corresponding point on the next
    wave; crest—the highest point on a
    wave; trough—the lowest point on
    a wave

59. 1. 420 m/s; 2. 2.0 m; 3. 4.3×10^{14}
    hertz; 4. 4×10^{-7} m; 5. 2 m/s

60. 1.   2.
    3.   4.

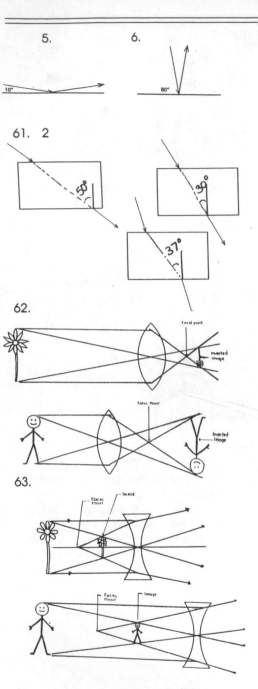

5. **6.**

66.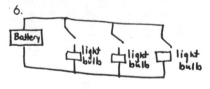

61. 2

62.

63.

64. a. red; b. orange; c. yellow; d. green; e. blue; f. indigo; g. violet

65. 1. j; 2. g; 3. d; 4. k; 5. m; 6. b; 7. o; 8. h; 9. n; 10. i; 11. f; 12. e; 13. p; 14. a; 15. l; 16. c

67. 1. 0.09 amps; 2. 0.48 amps; 3. 2.4 amps; 4. 4.8 amps; 5. 1.2 amps

68. 1. 1,000 volts; 2. 0.0198 volts; 3. 0.0523 volts; 4. 25,000 volts; 5. 0.0344 volts

69. 1. 10 ohms; 2. 0.48 ohms; 3. 4.5 ohms; 4. 0.002 ohms; 5. 150 ohms

70. 1. 1,200 amperes; 2. 0.05 ohms; 3. 0.2 volts; 4. 45,000 amps; 5. 6,250 volts

71. 1. 3 watts; 2. 83 volts; 3. 4.2 amps; 4. 75 watts; 5. 2.5 volts

72. 1. 0.55 kWh; 2. $0.06; 3. 4.4 kWh; 4. $0.44; 5. 59.4 kWh; 6. $8.91

73. 1. A. series; B. parallel; 2. no; 3. yes; 4. no; 5. yes

6.

7.

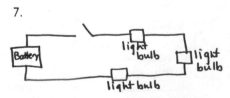

8. parallel; If one bulb burns out, the others will still light. This would not be true for series.

74. Step-Up—12 volts, 60 amps; Step-Down—4 volts, 360 amps

75. 1. 6.25 g; 2. 8.75 g; 3. 15.6 g; 4. 400 g; 5. 800 g; 6. 2.7 days